Letts

KS2
Success
Workbook

Lynn Huggins-Cooper

English
SATs

Contents

National Test practice

Answers

See additional answer booklet

Research

Research for an article

Carry out some research on extreme sports – and write a magazine article.

Research for a leaflet

Research into entertainment facilities for kids near you – and create a leaflet.

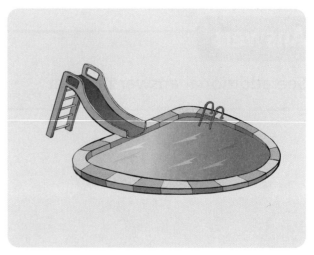

Research for a web page

Find out about your favourite animal – and build a free web page!

Research for a report

Do some research on your favourite computer game. Are there any clubs or 'cheat' sites on the Internet about your game? Write a report on it.

I'm going to the climbing wall to find out more!

Is that research – or just good fun?

The language of books

The words used with books

Answer these questions.

1 What is an ISBN number?

_____

2 What is it used for?

_____

3 Whereabouts on a book would you find it?

_____

4 What is blurb?

_____

5 What does an author do?

_____

6 What does an illustrator do?

_____

More terms

Now answer these questions.

1 What is an appendix used for? What would you find in an appendix?

_____

_____

2 What is a glossary used for?

_____

3 Can you describe what is meant by non-fiction?

_____

4 Can you describe what fiction means?

_____

5 What is an index?

_____

6 What are footnotes and whereabouts would you find them?

_____

Parenthesis 1

Fill in the missing words using the words in the box below:

brackets afterthoughts parenthesis information interruptions writing

Parenthesis means words that are added in **1** _____

to a piece of **2** _____ to give us more

3 _____. Sometimes the words in

4 _____ are explanations. Brackets can also be used to add

5 _____ and **6** _____.

Parenthesis 2

Look at these examples of words used in parenthesis and decide whether they are explanations or afterthoughts. Mark explanations with E and afterthoughts with A.

1 The boy (who had already been to the cinema) said that the film was hilarious. ☐

2 The cat (who had hidden a mouse under the cushion) looked smug. ☐

3 I will be on the school team this year (I hope!). ☐

4 The teacher (who already looked furious) threatened that he would get cross if anyone else spoke. ☐

5 'I love toffees!' she said (and grabbed a huge fistful). ☐

Isn't a glossary the stuff girls put on their lips?

No, silly! If you don't know what it means, look it up in the glossary!

Description and imagery

Write your own similes

Write a simile for each of these objects.

1 sea   _____

2 sun   _____

3 cat   _____

4 worm _____

5 spider _____

6 bat   _____

 Top Tip

*Remember, a metaphor is when something is described as something else; a simile is when it is described as **like** something else.*

Sam is as stinky as manure!

And Mel is as mean as a rattlesnake!

Write your own metaphors

Write a metaphor for each of these things.

1 baby's skin _____

2 strawberry _____

3 ladybird _____

4 ice cube _____

5 grass _____

6 moonlight _____

Personification

Match the personification description to the correct word.

1 Autumn

is a chubby little boy, dressed in green. His moods change from the temper of the blustering wind to the warmth of a sunny smile in minutes!

2 Snow

is a woman with copper hair and a dress made from leaves.

is a beautiful lady dressed in diamonds and white fur.

3 Spring

Top Tip *Read lots of poetry to find examples of personification, metaphors and similes.*

Alliteration and onomatopoeia

Find the alliteration

Underline the words that alliterate in each sentence.

1 Slimy slugs slide across the path.

2 Pink pigs prefer to eat potatoes.

3 Dreadful, dangerous dragons breathe flames.

4 Ghastly, gruesome ghouls groan in haunted castles.

5 Cheeky chipmunks chirrup at the birds as they steal their nuts.

Think up words

Think of words that alliterate with 'sun' and 'moon'. Write them in the shapes.

Match the words

Match the words that alliterate – and make the most sense!

1 slimy   girls

2 sizzling   foxes

3 furry   slugs

4 sparkling   sausages

5 giggling   sea

Top Tip

You often find examples of alliteration in the titles of books or films – look out for examples!

Find the onomatopoeia

Circle the words that are onomatopoeic.

pop   come   slurp

              smash

leg

                                     crash

wobble   table   cat

I can use alliteration better than my swotty sister!

No you can't, you bothersome, beastly brother!

Special words

Idioms

Use the words in the box below to complete the idioms:

finger   biscuit   hot   weather

1   He is feeling under the _____.

2   She can wrap her grandad around her little _____.

3   That man is always blowing _____ and cold.

4   You really take the _____!

Explain the idiom

Explain the meaning of each idiom.

1   Under the weather. _____

_____

2   Taking the biscuit. _____

_____

3   Blowing hot and cold. _____

_____

4   Keep your hair on! _____

_____

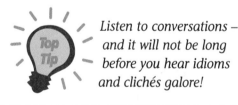

*Listen to conversations –
and it will not be long
before you hear idioms
and clichés galore!*

Matching proverbs

Match the beginnings and endings of these proverbs.

1   A stitch in time   is worth two in the bush.

2   Too many cooks   saves nine.

3   A bird in the hand   spoil the broth.

What proverbs mean

Explain what these proverbs mean.

1 A stitch in time saves nine.

_____

_____

2 Too many cooks spoil the broth.

_____

_____

3 A bird in the hand is worth two in the bush.

_____

_____

Clichés

Match the beginnings and endings of these clichés.

1	It's raining	the day.
2	At the end of	a parrot.
3	Starting on a	cats and dogs.
4	As sick as	level playing field.

What do you mean, 'take the biscuit'? What have I done?

Nothing – I was just offering you a chocolate finger!

Ambiguity

Spot the real meaning!

Read these sentences. What do you think the writer means in each case?

1 The dog chased the cat, because it was bored. (Which animal was bored? Was the dog trying to cheer the cat up, because she was bored, or was the dog looking for mischief because he was bored?)

_____

2 If that dog doesn't want his dinner, throw it away!

_____

3 The mother scolded the girl, because she was being nasty.

_____

Making sense

Fill in the missing words using the words in the box below:

> ambiguous   clear   sentences   unclear   pronouns

If the meaning of a sentence is **1** _____, it is

2 _____. Sometimes, **3** _____ are ambiguous,

because the **4** _____ such as he and she are badly placed. It is

important to make your meaning **5** _____.

Imagine if you said, 'If that cat doesn't want her food, throw it away,' and your mum threw the cat in the bin!

Make it clear!

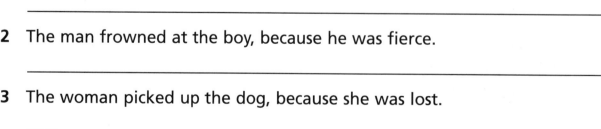

Rewrite the sentences to make the meaning clear.

1 The fox ate the rabbit, because it was hungry.

_____

2 The man frowned at the boy, because he was fierce.

_____

3 The woman picked up the dog, because she was lost.

_____

Using the words

Answer these questions.

1   What do people mean when they say that a sentence is ambiguous?

_____

_____

2   Why is it important to make your meaning clear?

_____

3   Which type of word can make a sentence ambiguous if you are not careful?

_____

More on making it clear!

Rewrite these sentences to make the meaning clear.

1   The monkey chased the butterfly, because it was beautiful.

_____

2   Shushi decided that the dog's collar was too big, so she sold it.

_____

3   The leak was repaired before much damage could be done by the man.

_____

4   The shark ate the fish, because it was huge.

_____

 Top Tip *Sometimes, meaning becomes unclear, because the sentence you are writing goes on and on… It is better to use shorter sentences to make your meaning clear. Be careful where you put pronouns, too!*

School? I'm ambiguous about it…

I don't think the headteacher is ambiguous about you!

Reading investigation

Build a bookbug!

You are going to make an ever-growing bookbug about the books you read.

It will make a great display for your bedroom wall, or you could ask your mum or dad if you can put it up in the kitchen!

What to do

Make a head for your bug out of paper scraps, sweet wrappers and card. Be as imaginative as possible. You could make it look like a caterpillar or a worm, or even an alien!

Make the head about the size of a cereal packet. If you are feeling very arty, you can make a 3D head by using boxes and packages – but don't make it too heavy, or you will not be able to attach it to the wall.

If you use cardboard packaging, take the boxes apart and turn them inside out before using them – plain card is easier to paint.

Every time you read a book, make another segment for your bookbug. You could stick on sequins, beads, feathers – in fact, anything you think of – round the edges.

Top Tip *See how long you can make your bookbug. You could even ask friends and family members to add their own reviews.*

Fiction segment

If the book you have read is fiction, include this information in the segment.

- Title of book:
- Author:
- Illustrator (if applicable):
- Favourite characters:
- Main problem or issue:
- Was there a message in the story?
- Was there a twist in the tail?

Non-fiction segment

If the book you have read is non-fiction, include this information in the segment.

- Title of book:
- Author:
- Illustrator (if applicable):
- How much information did you learn from this book?
- How easy was it to find the information you wanted?
- Was there a glossary?
- How hard/easy was the book to read?

I'm going to make a huge alien with segmented tentacles!

Are you going to look in the mirror to get some ideas?

Contractions

Missing words

Fill in the missing words using the words in the box below:

> friends   apostrophe   missed   speaking
>
> letters   formal   informal

Contractions are words that have **1** _____ missing.

An **2** _____ shows where the letters have been **3** _____

out. Words like this are used in **4** _____ writing, such as:

- Letters to **5** _____

- When a character in a story is **6** _____

Contractions are not used in pieces of **7** _____ writing, such as

reports or business letters.

Contractions in full

Write these contractions in their full form. For example: *I've* becomes *I have*.

1 won't _____   **4** they're _____

2 can't _____   **5** don't _____

3 you've _____   **6** she'll _____

Matching contractions

Match these words to their contractions.

1	I cannot	don't
2	I am	I'd
3	I have	I can't
4	we are	I'd
5	do not	I've
6	I had	we're
7	I would	I'm

Remember, contractions can be used in informal writing, like letters to friends. They should not be used for formal work.

Shorten the words

Rewrite these sentences, using contractions wherever possible.

1   The boys would not go to bed.

_____

2   I will not be able to come to the party.

_____

3   We are going out now.

_____

4   You have got to be quiet!

_____

5   I am going to the shops now.

_____

Take away the contractions

Rewrite these sentences so that they do not contain contractions.

1   I can't do it!

_____

2   I wouldn't like to go anywhere cold.

_____

3   No it's not!

_____

4   It doesn't matter.

_____

5   I've got a huge bowl of sweets.

_____

So a contraction is where letters are missing?

Like the ones you never write back to your pen pal?

Apostrophes

Apostrophe + s

Rewrite these phrases to add a possessive apostrophe. For example: *The bowl that belongs to the cat* becomes *The cat's bowl.*

1   The ball that belongs to the baby _____

2   The hat that belongs to the man _____

3   The coat that belongs to the girl _____

4   The bag of sweets that belongs to the teacher _____

5   The collar that belongs to the dog _____

Words that already end with s

When a word already ends in -s, the apostrophe is sometimes added without adding another -s. For example: *The sister belonging to James* becomes *James' sister*. This is called the possessive apostrophe.

Rewrite these sentences adding a possessive apostrophe.

1   The cats paws were pink. _____

2   The ladies hats were all huge. _____

3   The girls bikes were new. _____

4   The boys trousers were all blue. _____

More possessive apostrophes

Rewrite these phrases, putting in the possessive apostrophes.

1   The favourite shirts of the men _____

2   The house of Stefan _____

3   The food of the geese _____

4   The boots of the gardeners _____

5   The school of the children _____

Add the apostrophes

Rewrite the sentences, adding the possessive apostrophes.

1 The cats tail curled around her bottom, like a snakes coils.

_____

2 The dogs looked excited when they saw the cats whiskers.

_____

3 The lions warm breath blew down the back of the mens necks.

_____

4 The neighbours houses had a shared front garden.

_____

Is the apostrophe right?

Put a tick or cross to show if these possessive apostrophes are in the right place.

1 Kate's rabbit ☐   **4** The cats' whiskers ☐

2 Hassans' jumper ☐   **5** The mice's cheese ☐

3 The mens' cars ☐

Is it *its* or *it's*?

Circle the correct word – *its* or *it's*.

1   Its / It's   a beautiful day!

2   Its / It's   not fair!

3   What is   its / it's   name?

4   The horse has escaped again.
    Go and shut   its / it's   gate!

Top Tip *Make sure you learn where to use its and it's – people often get this wrong!*

It's not fair – Mel won't lend me her books!

That's because I'm as possessive over them as you are over your computer games!

Punctuation

Using punctuation

Put full stops and capital letters in this passage so it makes sense.

the woman looked surprised surely she had not heard the cat speak! she ought to rest more it must be overwork that was making her hear things if she was not careful, people would start thinking she was bonkers of course, she would never tell anyone what she thought she had heard cats meow, of course, but they do not usually strike up conversations with people!

Exclamation marks and question marks

Which is it? Should it be a question mark or exclamation mark? You decide!

1   What is the time

2   "Who's eaten my ice cream " bellowed Dad, angrily.

3   Can I come too

4   "Dreadful boy " shouted the angry girl.

5   What do you mean

Top Tip

If you are writing something and you are not sure if a sentence should end in a question mark, read it out loud. If it sounds like a question, add a question mark!

Commas

Commas are used to divide different parts of a sentence and help to make the meaning clear. Rewrite these sentences using commas so they make sense.

1   When the party was over the people went home.

_____

2   I like toffee chocolate vanilla and strawberry ice-cream.

_____

3   "What a pretty name" Shireen told Frances.

_____

4   The crocodile shot out of the water snapping as it went.

_____

Commas in lists

Put the commas in the right places in these lists.

1 The dog was a huge dirty shaggy mess.

2 I'd like a bar of chocolate some sherbet a lolly and an ice-cream please.

3 I've had two colds flu a fever and measles this winter!

4 The spider was huge hairy black and totally terrifying!

Semicolons

Semicolons can be used to break up lists, or to divide clauses in a sentence. A semicolon can make two sentences into one. Write these sentences using semicolons.

1 I shut my eyes. Soon it would be morning.

_____

2 I would love to go on holiday somewhere hot. Bermuda would be my choice.

_____

3 The animals all came into the ark. They were desperate to shelter from the rain.

_____

Colons

Colons can be used to introduce an explanation, or to show that a list is about to begin. Add the colons to the following sentences.

1 You will need cardboard, sticky tape and paper clips.

2 When you get to the shops, I would like eggs, milk, flour, potatoes and some shoelaces.

3 The party was over everyone had gone home.

4 Ingredients chocolate, crispy cereal and treacle.

Writing about speech

Reported speech

Reported speech means someone is telling the reader about something somebody else has said. Rewrite these sentences as reported speech. For example: *"I like apples," said Mrs Harris* becomes *Mrs Harris said she liked apples.*

1 "I love dogs!" said Trevor.

_____

2 "Cats are the most intelligent creatures in the universe," said Professor Newton.

_____

3 Dave said, "I'm going on holiday next week – and I can't wait!"

_____

4 Sheila yelled, "Get off my cabbages, you silly pigeons!"

_____

5 "Well, I'd love to, thanks very much," Tina laughed.

_____

Direct speech

Direct speech is the actual words that people say. Rewrite this reported speech as direct speech.

1 The boy said he wanted to go home.

_____

2 The man told me that he liked mushroom pizza best.

_____

3 They told me that they hated school.

_____

4 Cory said that he had not enjoyed the museum.

_____

5 The old man asked the girl what the time was.

_____

Punctuation

Speech marks always end with a punctuation mark inside the speech marks.

If someone is surprised or shouting, use an exclamation mark. If it is a question, use a question mark. Add the correct punctuation to these sentences.

1   "I think that's a great idea ＿＿ " said Mr Nelson.

2   "Why can't I go, Mum ＿＿ " asked Beth.

3   "It's time for bed, Alice – now ＿＿ " called Dad.

4   "Is it dinnertime yet ＿＿ " asked Rajan.

Not just said, but...

Circle the words in the box that could be used instead of 'said'.

yelled   slid   jumped   screamed   walked   sniggered   leaped   whispered

hooted   swam   asked   groaned   waltzed   giggled   squealed   sighed

Reported or direct?

Work out and note if these sentences are reported speech (R) or direct speech (D).

1   "Can I go out now, Mum?"   ☐

2   She asked if she could go to the youth club.   ☐

3   "So what?" yelled the boy.   ☐

4   My mother told me I should always eat the right foods.   ☐

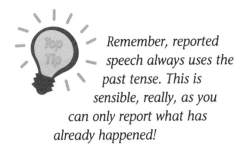

Remember, reported speech always uses the past tense. This is sensible, really, as you can only report what has already happened!

If people tell tales, is that reported speech?

I wouldn't know – I never tell tales, unlike SOME people I could mention...

Plurals

More than one

When you are writing or talking about more than one thing, it is called a plural. Usually, you just write a word and add an -s to the end to make it a plural. For example: *cat* becomes *cats*.

Add -s to make these words plural.

1 bird _____

2 flower _____

3 chair _____

4 boy _____

5 apple _____

6 snowflake _____

Tricky words

If a word already ends in -s, you cannot simply add another -s! Instead, you add -es. This is the same for words ending in -x. For example: *box* becomes *boxes*.

Add -es to these words to make them plural.

1 fox _____   **3** press _____

2 mess _____   **4** dress _____

Words ending in -y

Words that end in -y have special rules. Most words that end in -y lose the -y and add -ies. For example: *lady* becomes *ladies*.

Now try these.

1 pony _____   **4** fly _____

2 baby _____   **5** party _____

3 puppy _____   **6** country _____

Words ending in -f

When words end in -f and change from single to plural, there is a special rule: the -f changes to -ves. For example: *leaf* becomes *leaves*.

Now try these.

1 hoof _____

2 calf _____

3 dwarf _____

4 loaf _____

Words ending in -o

When words ending in -o are changed from single to plural, there is a special rule: the -o stays and -es is added. For example: *echo* becomes *echoes*.

Now try these.

1 tomato _____

2 tornado _____

3 potato _____

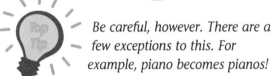

Be careful, however. There are a few exceptions to this. For example, piano becomes pianos!

The really odd ones!

Some plurals you just have to learn. It should not be hard, because they are quite odd!

Find the plurals of:

1 louse _____

2 child _____

3 formula _____

4 moose _____

5 goose _____

6 man _____

Ooh, scary thought – plural Mel!

Twice as nice!

Nouns and pronouns

What is a noun?

Nouns are naming words. The names of people, places, animals and things are all nouns. Underline the nouns.

1   The cat ran.

2   The cake was sweet.

3   The sky was dark.

4   The caterpillar changed.

5   The sun shone.

6   The dog barked.

Find the missing words

Fill in the missing words from the box below:

place   nouns   repeating   same   pronouns

What is a pronoun?

1 _____ do the same job as 2 _____. Words like he, she, it, mine and yours are all pronouns. They are used in the

3 _____ of nouns. They are very useful, because they stop you

from 4 _____ yourself. If your writing was full of the

5 _____ words being repeated, it could easily become dull!

Using pronouns

Read the sentences below. Circle the correct nouns or pronouns to make the writing flow more easily.

1   Warren / He ate some cake, because Warren / he / him liked chocolate cake most of all. Warren / He ate it every chance that Warren / he / him got.

2   Mitzi / She went swimming, because that was Mitzi's / she / her favourite sport. Mitzi / She tried to go swimming every day, because Mitzi / she / her thought it would keep Mitzi / she / her healthy.

3   Harvey / He goes to school and Harvey / he / him likes school very much. Harvey / He likes doing science best of all, because Harvey / he / him likes learning about animals.

Letts

KS2 Success

Workbook Answer Booklet

English

KS2 SATs

Reading

PAGES 4–5 RESEARCH

Research for an article

research carried out properly and presented in the form of an article

Research for a leaflet

research carried out properly and presented in the form of a leaflet

Research for a web page

research carried out properly and presented in the form of a web page

Research for a report

research carried out properly and presented in the form of a report

PAGES 6–7 THE LANGUAGE OF BOOKS

The words used with books

1 a long number on the back of a book used to catalogue or order it
2 to find or order a book
3 at the back
4 information on the back of a book to make you want to read it
5 writes books
6 draws pictures to illustrate books

More terms

1 An appendix is used to give the reader more information about a particular subject raised in a book; it is a collection of extra material, found at the end of a book.
2 to give the meanings of words, a little like a dictionary
3 writing that is not 'made up'
4 'made up' writing, not real-life stories
5 an alphabetical list of contents in a book that helps the reader to find particular subjects
6 extra bits of information or explanations found at the bottom of a page

Parenthesis 1

1 brackets
2 writing
3 information
4 parenthesis
5 interruptions/afterthoughts
6 afterthoughts/interruptions

Parenthesis 2

1 E   2 E   3 A   4 E   5 A

PAGES 8–9 DESCRIPTION AND IMAGERY

Write your own similes

For example:

1 like foaming bath water
2 like a glowing orange, thrown into the sky
3 like a tiger stalking her prey
4 like a coiling snake
5 like a troll waiting under a bridge
6 like a mouse in a hang-glider

Write your own metaphors

For example:

1 is a flower petal
2 is a ruby
3 is a cherry
4 is a tiny iceberg
5 is an emerald carpet
6 is liquid honey

Personification

1 Autumn → is a woman with copper hair and a dress made from leaves.
2 Snow → is a beautiful lady dressed in diamonds and white fur.
3 Spring → is a chubby little boy, dressed in green. His moods change from the temper of the blustering wind to the warmth of a sunny smile in minutes!

PAGES 10–11 ALLITERATION AND ONOMAOTAPOEIA

Find the alliteration

1 <u>Slimy slugs slide</u> across the path.
2 <u>Pink pigs prefer</u> to eat <u>potatoes</u>.
3 <u>Dreadful, dangerous dragons</u> breathe flames.
4 <u>Ghastly, gruesome ghouls groan</u> in haunted castles.
5 <u>Cheeky chipmunks chirrup</u> at the birds as they steal their nuts.

Think up words

words that alliterate with 'sun' in the sun shape; words that alliterate with 'moon' in the moon shape

Match the words

1 slimy → slugs
2 sizzling → sausages
3 furry → foxes
4 sparkling → sea
5 giggling → girls

Find the onomatopoeia

Circled words are:

pop, smash, slurp, wobble and crash.

PAGES 12–13 SPECIAL WORDS

Idioms

1 weather   3 hot

2 finger   4 biscuit

Explain the idiom

1 not feeling very well

2 outrageous; the last word in cheek

3 sometimes friendly, sometimes not – very changeable

4 Calm down!

Matching proverbs

1 A stitch in time ➜ saves nine.

2 Too many cooks ➜ spoil the broth.

3 A bird in the hand ➜ is worth two in the bush.

What proverbs mean

1 Putting things right straight away saves time and effort later.

2 Involving too many people can make things difficult to do.

3 A sure thing is better than many things that you may achieve.

Clichés

1 It's raining ➜ cats and dogs

2 At the end of ➜ the day

3 Starting on a ➜ level playing field

4 As sick as ➜ a parrot

PAGES 14–15 AMBIGUITY

Spot the real meaning!

1 The dog was bored.

2 Throw the dinner away if the dog doesn't want to eat it.

3 The girl was being nasty, so her mother scolded her.

Making sense

1 unclear/ambiguous

2 ambiguous/unclear

3 sentences

4 pronouns

5 clear

Make it clear!

Many answers are possible, for instance:

1 The fox was hungry, so he/she ate the rabbit.

2 The man was fierce, so he frowned at the boy.

3 The dog was lost, so the woman picked him up.

Using the words

1 When a sentence is ambiguous, the meaning is unclear and could mean more than one thing.

2 Ambiguous statements can lead to confusion.

3 a pronoun

More on making it clear!

Many answers are possible, for instance:

1 The butterfly was beautiful, so the monkey chased it.

2 Shushi decided that the dog's collar was too big, so she sold the collar.

3 The leak was repaired by the man before much damage could be done.

4 The huge shark ate the fish.

PAGES 16–17 READING INVESTIGATION

a completed bookbug!

Writing

PAGES 18–19 CONTRACTIONS

Missing words

1 letters

2 apostrophe

3 missed

4 informal

5 friends

6 speaking

7 formal

Contractions in full

1 will not   4 they are

2 cannot   5 do not

3 you have   6 she will

Matching contractions

1 I cannot ➜ I can't

2 I am ➜ I'm

3 I have ➜ I've

4 we are ➜ we're

5 do not → don't
6 I had → I'd
7 I would → I'd

Shorten the words
1 The boys **wouldn't** go to bed.
2 I **won't** be able to come to the party.
3 **We're** going out now.
4 **You've** got to be quiet!
5 **I'm** going to the shops now.

Take away the contractions
1 I **cannot** do it!
2 I **would not** like to go anywhere cold.
3 No **it is** not!
4 It **does not** matter.
5 **I have** a huge bowl of sweets.

PAGES 20–21 APOSTROPHES
Apostrophe + s
1 The baby's ball.
2 The man's hat.
3 The girl's coat.
4 The teacher's sweets.
5 The dog's collar.

Words that already end with s
1 The cats' paws were pink.
2 The ladies' hats were all huge.
3 The girls' bikes were new.
4 The boys' trousers were all blue.

More possessive apostrophes
1 the men's shirts
2 Stefan's house
3 the geese's food
4 the gardeners' boots
5 the children's school

Add the apostrophes
1 cat's tail/snake's coils
2 cat's whiskers (or cats' whiskers)
3 lion's warm breath/men's necks
4 neighbours' houses

Is the apostrophe right?
1 ✔ 2 ✗ 3 ✗ 4 ✔ 5 ✔

Is it *its* or *it's*?
1 It's 2 It's 3 its 4 its

PAGES 22–23 PUNCTUATION
Using punctuation
The woman looked surprised. **S**urely she had not heard the cat speak! **S**he ought to rest more. **I**t must be overwork that was making her hear things. **I**f she was not careful, people would start thinking she was bonkers. **O**f course, she would never tell anyone what she thought she had heard. **C**ats meow, of course, but they do not usually strike up conversations with people!

Exclamation marks and question marks
1 ? 2 ? 3 ? 4 ! 5 ?

Commas
1 When the party was over, the people went home.
2 I like toffee, chocolate, vanilla and strawberry ice-cream.
3 "What a pretty name," Shireen told Frances.
4 The crocodile shot out of the water, snapping as it went.

Commas in lists
1 The dog was a huge, dirty, shaggy mess.
2 I'd like a bar of chocolate, some sherbet, a lolly and an ice-cream please.
3 I've had two colds, flu, a fever and measles this winter!
4 The spider was huge, hairy, black and totally terrifying!

Semicolons
1 I shut my eyes; soon it would be morning.
2 I would love to go on holiday somewhere hot; Bermuda would be my choice.
3 The animals all came into the ark; they were desperate to shelter from the rain.

Colons
1 You will need: cardboard, sticky tape and paper clips.
2 When you get to the shops, I would like: eggs, milk, flour, potatoes and some shoelaces.
3 The party was over: everyone had gone home.
4 Ingredients: chocolate, crispy cereal and treacle.

PAGES 24–25 WRITING ABOUT SPEECH
Reported speech
1 Trevor said that he loved dogs.
2 Professor Newton said that cats were the most intelligent creatures in the universe.
3 Dave said that he was going on holiday next week and he couldn't wait.
4 Sheila yelled at the pigeons that they were silly and they should get off her cabbages.
5 Tina laughed and said she would love to and then said thanks very much.

Direct speech

1 "I want to go home," said the boy.
2 "I like mushroom pizza best," the man told me.
3 "We hate school," they told me.
4 "I didn't enjoy the museum," said Cory.
5 "What time is it?" the old man asked the girl.

Punctuation

1 "I think that's a great idea**!**" said Mr Nelson.
2 "Why can't I go, Mum**?**" asked Beth.
3 "It's time for bed, Alice – now**!**" called Dad.
4 "Is it dinnertime yet**?**" asked Rajan.

Not just said, but…

Circled words are:
yelled, screamed, sniggered, whispered, hooted, asked, groaned, giggled, squealed and sighed.

Reported or direct?

1 D   **2** R   **3** D   **4** R

PAGES 26–27 PLURALS

More than one

1 birds
2 flowers
3 chairs
4 boys
5 apples
6 snowflakes

Tricky words

1 foxes
2 messes
3 presses
4 dresses

Words ending in -y

1 ponies
2 babies
3 puppies
4 flies
5 parties
6 countries

Words ending in -f

1 hooves
2 calves
3 dwarves
4 loaves

Words ending in -o

1 tomatoes
2 tornadoes
3 potatoes

The really odd ones!

1 lice   4 moose
2 children   5 geese
3 formulae   6 men

PAGES 28–29 NOUNS AND PRONOUNS

What is a missing words

1 The <u>cat</u> ran.
2 The <u>cake</u> was sweet.
3 The <u>sky</u> was dark.
4 The <u>caterpillar</u> changed.
5 The <u>sun</u> shone.
6 The <u>dog</u> barked.

Find the missing words

1 pronouns
2 nouns
3 place
4 repeating
5 same

Using pronouns

1 (Warren) ate some cake, because (he) liked chocolate cake most of all. (He) ate it every chance that (he) got.
2 (Mitzi) went swimming, because that was (her) favourite sport. (She) tried to go swimming every day, because (she) thought it would keep (her) healthy.
3 (Harvey) goes to school and (he) likes school very much. (He) likes doing science best of all, because (he) likes learning about animals.

Be careful!

1 They
2 them
3 they
4 they
5 them
6 they

Make a pronouns collection

check the child's pronouns

Nouns and pronouns

1 The **cat (N)** meowed, because **she (P)** was hungry.
2 The **girl (N)** laughed, because **she (P)** was happy.
3 The **snake (N)** slithered away, because **it (P)** was scared.
4 The **spider (N)** scuttled off, because **it (P)** saw a hungry **bird (N)**.
5 **Susan (N)** and **Karim (N)** saw the **bus (N)**, so **they (P)** started to run.

PAGES 30–31 ADJECTIVES

What are adjectives?
1 The <u>tabby</u> cat
2 The <u>slippery</u> slug
3 The <u>enormous</u> doorway
4 The <u>magenta</u> ribbon
5 The <u>glittering</u> sea
6 The <u>loud</u>, <u>angry</u> man

Making your writing exciting
For example:
1 The fat, hairy spider hid in the darkness.
2 The huge, red balloon floated away into the sky.
3 The fragrant, pink flower grew in the garden.

Exciting options!
For example:
1 violet, lilac
2 crimson, scarlet
3 azure, sapphire
4 golden, honey
5 chocolate, coffee
6 navy, royal blue

It's not nice!
For example:
1 My grandad is really kind to me.
2 This ice-cream is delicious.
3 The weather is lovely today.
4 My cat's fur feels wonderful.
5 I thought the film was excellent.

Interesting alternatives
For example:
1 hilarious
2 tragic
3 vast
4 microscopic
5 intelligent
6 delicious

Dazzling descriptions!
For example:
1 speedy
2 sparkling
3 silken
4 vast
5 glittering
6 rubbery
7 molten
8 sporty
9 hideous
10 slippery

PAGES 32–33 VERBS AND ADVERBS

What are verbs?
1 The man <u>shouted</u>.
2 The girl <u>giggled</u>.
3 The shark <u>chewed</u>.
4 The bell <u>rang</u>.
5 The firework <u>fizzed</u>.

Passive verbs
1 The cat was (stroked.)
2 The paper was (folded.)
3 The dog was (walked.)
4 The girl was (taken) to school.
5 The baby was (cuddled)
6 The dinner was (cooked.)

Active verbs
1 I (stroked) the cat.
2 Dad (folded) the paper.
3 Alexander (walked) the dog.
4 Beth (took) the girl to school.
5 Ellie (cuddled) the baby.
6 Lily (cooked) the dinner.

Tenses
Many answers are possible, for instance:
1 I shall walk on the beach.
2 He will read a horror story.
3 I shall go Christmas shopping.
4 Susie will write to her friend.
5 The cat will sleep in front of the fire.

What are adverbs?
1 The lion roared <u>fiercely</u>.
2 The sun shone <u>brightly</u>.
3 The stream flowed <u>quickly</u>.
4 The snow fell <u>thickly</u>.
5 The woman smiled <u>warmly</u>.
6 The storm raged <u>angrily</u>.

More about adverbs
1 The boy was (quite) scruffy.
2 The cake was (completely) ruined.
3 The dress was (very) beautiful.
4 The sky was (totally) dark.
5 The baby was (completely) hysterical.
6 The snail was (extremely) slow.

PAGES 34–35 BUILDING VOCABULARY

Build your own thesaurus!
For example:

big: huge massive enormous gargantuan vast

small: tiny minuscule microscopic diminutive

walked: wandered ambled meandered

smelly: whiffy stinky pongy
happy: delighted joyful ecstatic

PAGES 36–37 WRITING ABOUT A PERSON

Biography
a short biography of an admired person

Autobiography
a short autobiography

CV
a CV with relevant facts

PAGES 38–39 WRITING INSTRUCTIONS

Instructions
step-by-step instructions, correctly ordered, for making a card. Language used should be suitable for a younger child.

Recipes
step-by-step instructions, correctly ordered, for making lollies

PAGES 40–41 PERSUASIVE WRITING

Design a leaflet
completed leaflet, attractively set out on the subject of keeping a pet

Design a poster
attractive poster about band/TV show using persuasive language

PAGES 42–43 WRITING REPORTS

Writing reports for science
a report clearly describing the habitat chosen and the animals and plants that live there

Writing reports for geography
a geography report about the local area with lots of information about facilities available

PAGES 44–45 WRITING RECOUNTS

Recounting a game
a recount of a game played, including any funny anecdotes and the way the game ended

Recounting a film
a recount of the story of a film that has been watched and enjoyed – perhaps including the reasons why it was enjoyed

PAGES 46–47 WRITING STORIES
story written using the planning stages provided

PAGES 48–49 WRITING INVESTIGATION

Haiku
a haiku using the 5, 7, 5 pattern successfully

Kennings
an interesting, descriptive kenning for others to guess

National Test practice

PAGES 50–56 NATIONAL TEST PRACTICE

Reading task
1 Thane of Glamis
2 three witches
3 King
4 his sons will be kings
5 because she and Macbeth could kill him there
6 hags, crones
7 Macbeth meets the witches with Banquo as they return from battle.
King Duncan is murdered.
Macduff's family is killed.
Lady Macbeth goes mad.
Macbeth's head is taken to Malcolm.
8 Macduff's soldiers disguise themselves with twigs and branches from Great Birnam Wood, making it look as if the wood is moving towards Dunsinane castle.
9 guilt from killing King Duncan; she washes invisible blood from her hands, then kills herself
10 many answers are possible

Writing task
1 a suitable plan, such as a flow chart or similar, and a recount of a day out
2 a suitable story plan and character ideas, plus a story with a strong beginning, good development and a strong ending

Letts and Lonsdale
4 Grosvenor Place
London SW1X 7DL
Orders: 015395 64910

Enquiries: 015395 65921
Email: enquiries@lettsandlonsdale.co.uk
Website: www.lettsandlonsdale.com

First published 2007

Editorial and design: 2ibooks [publishing solutions] Cambridge

Colour Reprographics by PDQ

Author: Lynn Huggins-Cooper
Book concept and development: Helen Jacobs, Publishing Director
Project editor: Lily Morgan
Illustrators: Piers Baker and Pumpkin House
Cover design: Angela English

Every effort has been made to trace copyright holders and obtain their permission for the use of copyright material. The authors and publishers will gladly receive information enabling them to rectify any error or omission in subsequent editions.

All facts are correct at time of going to press.

British Library Cataloging in Publication Data. A CIP record of this book is available from the British Library.

9781843157496

Text, design and illustration © 2006 Letts Educational Limited

Letts and Lonsdale make every effort to ensure that all paper used in our books is made from wood pulp obtained from well-managed forests, controlled sources and recycled wood or fibre.

Be careful!

They and *them* are easy to mix up and so are *me* and *my*, so be careful. Circle the correct word in each sentence.

1   Them / They are lovely!

2   Do you like them / they?

3   Why are them / they going home?

4   What are them / they going to do?

5   What is wrong with them / they?

6   When are them / they arriving?

Make a pronouns collection

Pronouns are really useful words. You will already be using these words without realising that they are pronouns. The only new thing you need to learn is that they are called pronouns. For example: he, she, it, mine, yours, I, you, we, they, me, him, her, them and us.

To learn which words are pronouns, learn them like spellings.

Remember to read your work back to yourself. This will make sure you have not kept repeating nouns when a pronoun would make the work flow more naturally.

Nouns and pronouns

Mark the nouns (N) and the pronouns (P) in each sentence.

1   The cat ____ meowed, because she ____ was hungry.

2   The girl ____ laughed, because she ____ was happy.

3   The snake ____ slithered away, because it ____ was scared.

4   The spider ____ scuttled off, because it ____ saw a hungry bird ____.

5   Susan ____ and Karim ____ saw the bus ____, so they ____ started to run.

Sam's a noun!

And known by my friends and me as it – a pronoun!

Adjectives

What are adjectives?

Adjectives are describing words. (They describe a noun in a sentence.)
Underline the adjectives.

1   The tabby cat   2   The slippery slug   3   The enormous doorway

4   The magenta ribbon   5   The glittering sea   6   The loud, angry man

Making your writing exciting

Adjectives are a powerful tool for a writer. They are
describing words, and exciting descriptions are what
make people want to read more. Adjectives help to
make vivid word pictures in the mind of your readers.

Top Tip *Try to use unusual adjectives. Collect them in a notebook when you are reading.*

Compare these sentences:

The bear growled at the girls.

The ferocious black bear growled at the cowering girls.

Which sentence makes the best word picture? The sentence with adjectives,
of course! Rewrite these sentences using adjectives to make them more
interesting.

1   The spider hid in the darkness. _____

    _____

2   The balloon floated away into the sky. _____

    _____

3   The flower grew in the garden. _____

    _____

Exciting options!

Why say pink when you can say magenta? Think of a more exciting adjective
to replace each colour word.

1   The flower is purple _____   4   The sun is yellow _____

2   The apple is red _____   5   The mud is brown _____

3   The sea is blue _____   6   The jacket is blue _____

It's not nice!

Nice is a rather dull, overused adjective. Think of a more interesting adjective to replace nice in each sentence.

1 My grandad is really nice to me. _____

2 This ice-cream is nice. _____

3 The weather is nice today. _____

4 My cat's fur feels nice. _____

5 I thought the film was nice. _____

Interesting alternatives

Choose a more interesting alternative for each adjective.

1 funny _____   4 small _____

2 sad _____   5 clever _____

3 big _____   6 tasty _____

Dazzling descriptions

Choose a suitable adjective to describe each of these nouns.

1 horse _____   6 balloons _____

2 snow _____   7 chocolate _____

3 butterfly _____   8 car _____

4 elephant _____   9 alien _____

5 stars _____   10 snail _____

You're not very nice sometimes, Mel!

No, you mean I'm vile – that's much more descriptive!

Verbs and adverbs

What are verbs?

Verbs are words that describe actions. Every sentence has to have a verb or it is not a sentence. Verbs tell you what a person or thing is doing. For example, in the sentence: *The fish is swimming*, the word *swimming* is the verb.

Underline the verbs.

1 The man shouted.

2 The girl giggled.

3 The shark chewed.

4 The bell rang.

5 The firework fizzed.

Passive verbs

Passive verbs tell you about what is being done. A sentence with a passive verb tells you about the thing or person that the action is happening to. It does not always say what or who is doing the action, though. For example, in the sentence: *'The window was polished'*, we do not know who did the polishing.

Circle the verbs.

1 The cat was stroked.

2 The paper was folded.

3 The dog was walked.

4 The girl was taken to school.

5 The baby was cuddled.

6 The dinner was cooked.

Active verbs

Active verbs tell you what is being done and who is doing it. For example, in the sentence, *'Marie polished the window'*, we know who polished the window – Marie.

Circle the verbs.

1 I stroked the cat.

2 Dad folded the paper.

3 Alexander walked the dog.

4 Beth took the girl to school.

5 Ellie cuddled the baby.

6 Lily cooked the dinner.

Tenses

Verbs change tense to show us when things happen – whether it is past, present (now) or future. For example:

- I ate the pizza. *Past*
- I am eating the pizza. *Present (now)*
- I shall eat the pizza. *Future*

Rewrite the verbs in the future tense.

1   I walked on the beach.   _____

2   He is reading a horror story.   _____

3   I went Christmas shopping.   _____

4   Susie is writing to her friend.   _____

5   The cat is sleeping in front of the fire. _____

What are adverbs?

Adverbs are words that describe verbs. For example, in the sentence: *The shark swam quickly*, the word *quickly* is the adverb. It describes the verb *swam*, telling us how it was done.

Underline the adverbs.

1   The lion roared fiercely.   4   The snow fell thickly.

2   The sun shone brightly.   5   The woman smiled warmly.

3   The stream flowed quickly.   6   The storm raged angrily.

More about adverbs

Adverbs can also describe adjectives. Words like *completely*, *totally*, *quite* and *very* are used with adjectives to show how much the adjective is working on the noun. For example, in the sentence: *The woman was very cross*, the word *very* describes how cross she was.

Circle the adverbs that describe these adjectives.

1   The boy was quite scruffy.   4   The sky was totally dark.

2   The cake was completely ruined.   5   The baby was completely hysterical.

3   The dress was very beautiful.   6   The snail was extremely slow.

Building vocabulary

Build your own thesaurus!

A thesaurus is a book that gives the reader lots of different ways to say the same word. It helps writers to avoid their work becoming repetitive and boring.

For example, instead of said, you could use: *sighed, chuckled, laughed, bellowed, shouted* or *hooted*. Make a collection of interesting ways of saying:

Top Tip

Look in books and magazines as you are reading and make a collection of useful words in a notebook. You could arrange it in sections according to subject, for example space, animals or sea creatures.

Big

Not just big but…

_____

_____

_____

_____

_____

_____

_____

Small

Not just small but…

_____

_____

_____

_____

_____

_____

_____

Walked

Not just walked but...

_____

_____

_____

_____

_____

Smelly

Not just smelly but...

_____

_____

_____

_____

_____

Happy

Not just happy but...

_____

_____

_____

_____

_____

Of course, my vocabulary is gargantuan...

No, that's just your mouth!

Writing about a person

Biography

Write a short biography of a person you admire – in the news or in history.

_____
_____
_____
_____
_____
_____
_____
_____
_____
_____
_____
_____
_____

Autobiography

Write a short autobiography of your life so far!

_____
_____
_____
_____
_____
_____
_____
_____
_____
_____
_____
_____
_____

CV

Write your CV, as though you were applying for a job.

When you are writing a biography or autobiography, start with a timeline and work from there, adding details to each point on the timeline to build paragraphs.

My autobiography will be a very long book, because of all the brave deeds I've done...

It'll be very long, because it'll be so full of rubbish!

Writing instructions

Instructions

Imagine you are teaching a younger brother or sister how to make a birthday card for a relative. It could include pop-up pieces or a 'lift-the-flap'. Write a set of instructions to tell him/her what to do. Remember, provide a list of 'things you will need' as well as step-by-step instructions. If you are stumped for ideas, look in books or on the Internet.

_____
_____
_____
_____
_____
_____
_____
_____
_____
_____
_____
_____
_____
_____
_____
_____
_____
_____
_____
_____
_____

Remember that your instructions MUST be in the correct order.

Recipes

Write a recipe for making fruit ice lollies with juice and chunks of fruit.

_____

_____

_____

_____

_____

_____

_____

_____

_____

_____

_____

_____

_____

_____

_____

_____

_____

_____

_____

Let's make a card for grandad!

Aw...can't we just make lollies instead?!

Persuasive writing

Design a leaflet

Put together a leaflet about keeping an animal as a pet. It could be an animal you already have or one you would like, such as a tarantula. Carry out research to find out more, and then create a leaflet to encourage people to keep the animal as a pet.

please buy us.

We would you like to own a intellegent pet if you do come to micalle's pets come inside you such tallented pets.

all the animals you want just come to us to adopt a animal

come to th's place th's time right now.

10098take us.

we do not have dangerous animals.

please come or go on our website www.micalle's pets. or phone us 0207553351

come on!

you should tallented, cute, clever strained pet. so come

we do not have dangerous animals like tiger, or lion or cheta.

on offer

Animals

big to smal animals

Design a poster

Design a poster about your favourite band or TV show. Use persuasive language to provoke interest. Make your poster using a computer programme, and drag and drop photos or clip art onto the poster. Then print it out and hang it on the wall!

Top Tip

Bright colours and text boxes will help your writing to stand out so that people take notice.

I'm going to write a note to pursuade Mum to give me more pocket money!

Fat chance!

41

Writing reports

Writing reports for science

You often need to write reports in science. Choose a local habitat that you find interesting, such as the seashore, the garden or a pond, and write a report about it. Give details of the animals and plants that live there, and write something about their interesting habits. Look in books and on the Internet to find out more.

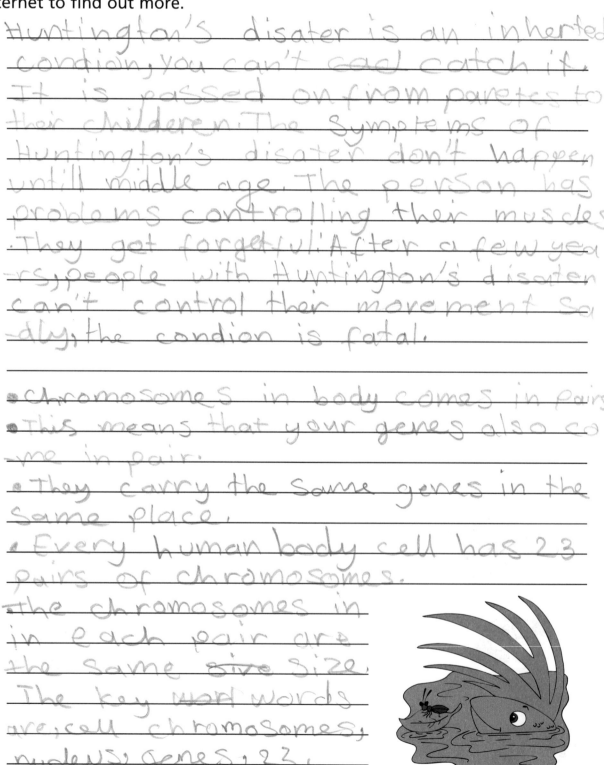

Huntington's disater is an inherted condion, you can't cacl catch it. It is passed on from paretes to their childeren. The symptems of Huntington's disater don't happen untill middle age. The person has problems controlling their muscles. They get forgetful. After a few years, people with Huntington's disater can't control their movement so dly, the condion is fatal.

• Chromosomes in body comes in pairs.
• This means that your genes also come in pair.
• They carry the same genes in the same place.
• Every human body cell has 23 pairs of chromosomes.
The chromosomes in in each pair are the same sive size. The key word words are, cell chromosomes, nucleus, genes, 23.

Writing reports for geography

Write a report about your local area. Are there lots of facilities for the community? Interview friends and family and find out what they think. You may even like to create a survey and report your findings. If your area has a local paper or newsletter, you could submit your report to them!

_____

_____

_____

_____

_____

_____

_____

_____

_____

_____

_____

_____

_____

_____

_____

_____

_____

_____

_____

_____

_____

_____

_____

_____

_____

_____

_____

_____

_____

Top Tip *Look in newsletters, magazines and newspapers to see examples of reports to remind you of the type of language used.*

Writing recounts

Recounting a game

Write a recount of the last game you played with your friends. It could be a game you played outside, a board game or a sport. Remember to say how the game ended!

_____

_____

_____

_____

_____

_____

_____

_____

_____

_____

_____

_____

_____

_____

_____

_____

_____

_____

_____

_____

_____

_____

_____

_____

_____

Recounting a film

Write a recount of a film you have enjoyed.

_____

_____

_____

_____

_____

_____

_____

_____

_____

_____

_____

_____

_____

_____

_____

_____

_____

_____

_____

_____

Top Tip *Don't forget to use words that tell the reader about the order in which things happened, such as 'next...then...finally'.*

I'm going to design a poster for *Cold Treason*. They're a great rock band!

I'll take some persuading...I prefer pop!

Writing stories

Write a story using one of these story starters

a   The noise filtered into my dream. It was a wailing, like something in pain...or something very scared. I woke with a start.

b   Jackie could not believe her luck. A whole month abroad! Nobody else she knew had ever been away for that long. This holiday was going to be amazing.

c   She watched the rain as it ran in channels down the cracked window. What a dump!

The best way to improve your story writing is to read more stories...so get down to the library!

Cluster of ideas and exciting vocabulary

Character profile

Problem for the characters to solve

_____
_____
_____
_____
_____
_____
_____

Good strong ending

_____
_____
_____
_____
_____
_____
_____

Now write your story!

A wailing, like something in pain? It must have been Sam, singing!

Cheek!

Writing investigation

Be a poet!

Poetry is a great source of descriptive and wonderful words. Look at the examples below.

> **Top Tip**
>
> *Try to read a variety of poems. Look for poetry collections in the library at school.*

Haiku

Haiku are Japanese poems with a special pattern of 17 syllables: 5, 7, 5. Have you read any haiku during the literacy hour at school?

Read this haiku:

> Beloved grey cat (5)
>
> Curls up softly in my lap (7)
>
> Funny, loyal friend. (5)

Now write your own haiku. You could write it about a pet or even about your favourite food.

Kennings

Kennings are a way of describing things without actually saying what they are. A poem can be made by making a list of kennings. Read this poem and try to guess what it is about!

Sticky-slitherer

Lettuce-eater

Mucus-bubbler

Glossy-egg-layer

Antennae-wiggler

Now write your own kennings poem. You could make a booklet with your poem on one side and the answer on the right-hand side under a flap, so people have to guess the answer!

I'd love to be a poet...

Well, you're certainly good at making things up!

National Test practice

Reading task

Mystery, murder and suspense – it is all to be found in Shakespeare's Macbeth!

Read the following synopsis, then answer the questions over the page.

Three foul witches meet on a wild, windswept heath. They are casting evil spells and incantations, and discussing the next time they will meet – and they reveal that Macbeth will be there.

Macbeth was the Thane of Glamis. He was a brave warrior, fighting as a champion of the King. Returning from the battle with his friend Banquo, he sees the witches. Cackling and mixing hideous potions, they predict that he will become first Thane of Cawdor, then King. They also say that Banquo will be father to Kings himself. Macbeth has ambitions, but he knows that King Duncan and his sons, Malcolm and Donalbain, are alive and well. Suddenly, they meet messengers from King Duncan who declare Macbeth Thane of Cawdor! The witches' prediction is beginning to come true, and Macbeth bubbles with excitement.

When they arrive at court, King Duncan declares that he has made his son, Malcolm, heir to the throne. Macbeth smiles, but feels sharp disappointment. Duncan then says that the royal party will travel to Macbeth's castle and spend the night there.

Macbeth dashes off ahead and tells his wife, Lady Macbeth. She is a cruel and ambitious woman. Since Macbeth sent her a letter telling her of the witches' prediction, she has been planning evil. Now she feels fate has played into her hands and tells Macbeth that the King should die in the night. Macbeth is shocked and shrinks from her. Lady Macbeth is a clever and persuasive woman and she manages to get her husband to agree to her plan. They are going to murder Duncan and blame his servants!

Macbeth waits until everyone is in bed, and creeps towards the King's chamber clutching his daggers. Suddenly, he sees a bloodstained dagger suspended in the air in front of him, but try as he might, he cannot grasp it. He sweeps into the King's chamber and commits the murder, coming back out clutching the daggers. Lady Macbeth takes the daggers from him and takes them back into the chamber so that the servants will be blamed.

A loud knocking sounds through the castle and the doors are opened to reveal Macduff. He needs to see the King. When he enters the chamber and finds the King dead, he runs out shouting for help. Macbeth kills the servants and this makes Macduff suspicious. Donalbain and Malcolm leave the castle, fearing for their own lives, and Macbeth is made King.

Macbeth worries that Banquo's sons will be Kings, as foretold by the witches, and that Banquo himself may suspect him of Duncan's murder. He decides to hold a banquet and invites Banquo. Banquo and his son ride out to hunt and Macbeth sends assassins after them. When the men return, they report that they have murdered Banquo but his son, Fleance, has escaped.

That night, Macbeth looks for his seat at the feast, saying that the table is full. He is shown a place, but all he can see is Banquo, with his throat slit. No one else can see the dreadful shadow. Macbeth is so worried that Lady Macbeth sends everyone away.

Later that night, Macbeth goes to see the witches. He is told by the hags that he should beware of Macduff and that Banquo's descendants will rule as Kings for generations. The crones also tell him that he will not be beaten until 'Great Birnam Wood shall come to Dunsinane'.

Macbeth sends assassins to kill Macduff, but he has already fled. They kill his family and Macduff swears revenge. He assembles an army and attacks Macbeth. Lady Macbeth has gone mad, and she walks the castle washing invisible blood from her hands. In her madness, she kills herself.

A messenger comes to say that Birnam Wood is attacking – all Macduff's men are carrying branches as cover. Macduff enters the castle and fights with Macbeth. Macduff slaughters Macbeth, the murderer, and cuts off his head. He takes it to Malcolm, the new King.

Choose the best words from the boxes to complete each sentence.

1   At the very beginning of the story, Macbeth is _____

> King of England   Thane of Cawdor   Thane of Glamis   very tired

2   Banquo and Macbeth meet _____

> three crows   three toads   three ghosts   three witches

3   The witches tell Macbeth that in the future he will be _____

> old   ill   King   Thane of Fife

4   Banquo is told that _____

> his sons will be killed   his sons will be soldiers
> his sons will be kings   his sons will be Thanes

5   Why was Lady Macbeth happy when she heard that King Duncan would sleep at her castle?

_____

_____

_____

6   Find two words in the story that have the same meaning as witches.

_____   _____

7   Put these events in order, numbering them from 1 to 5.

[ ]   King Duncan is murdered.

[ ]   Macbeth meets the witches with Banquo as they return from battle.

[ ]   Macduff's family is killed.

[ ]   Lady Macbeth goes mad.

[ ]   Macbeth's head is taken to Malcolm.

8 How did the hags' prediction about how the 'Great Birnam Wood shall come to Dunsinane' come true?

_____

_____

_____

_____

_____

_____

_____

9 Why do you think Lady Macbeth went mad? What did her madness make her do?

_____

_____

_____

_____

_____

_____

10 Did you enjoy the story? Give reasons to support your answers.

_____

_____

_____

_____

_____

_____

_____

Writing task

1 Write a recount of an exciting day out that you have enjoyed with friends or family. Don't forget to start with a plan, such as a flow diagram or a timeline.

Plan your recount here.

Now write your recount here.

_____

_____

_____

_____

_____

_____

_____

_____

_____

_____

_____

_____

_____

2 You are now going to practise planning and writing stories. Apart from being fun, you may choose to write a story for your SATs test.

Follow all the stages of writing a story:

clustering ideas

story plan

character profile

story starter

strong ending

Remember to ask yourself:

Where does your story begin?

Does the story setting help to build atmosphere? (For example, if it is a ghost story, is the story set in a spooky place?)

Who is going to appear in your story? Do you have a main character? Are there any heroes or villains?

Have you thought of a gripping beginning to hook your reader so that they want to read more?

How does the story develop? Are there any major changes or surprises during the story?

Have you done a character profile?

Have you thought of a good strong ending? Is there a twist in the tale (something unexpected at the end)?

Now plan your story here.

Now write your story here. Use spare paper if you need to.

_____

_____

_____

_____

_____

_____

_____

_____

_____

_____

_____

_____

_____

_____

_____

_____

_____

_____

_____

_____

_____

_____

_____

_____

_____

_____

_____